TRINITY
COLLEGE LONDON PRESS

C000170724

GRADE

04

TRUMPET
CORNET & FLUGELHORN

Pieces for Trinity College London
Exams 2019–2022

 Free downloads

Published by
Trinity College London Press Ltd
trinitycollege.com

Registered in England
Company no. 09726123

© Copyright 2018 Trinity College London Press Ltd
First impression, June 2018

Cover image courtesy of Yamaha Music Europe GmbH
Printed in England by Caligraving Ltd

Air

Henry Purcell
(1659-1695)
Arr. van Beringen

3

Samba-Cha

John Hawkins
(b. 1949)

Cassiopeia, Queen of the Stars

from *Constellations Set II*

Garry Wilkinson
(b. 1958)

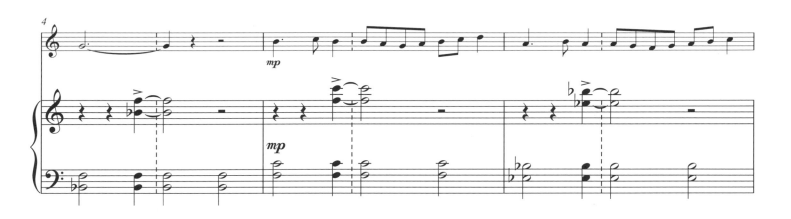

Last Dance

from *Offbeat Suite*

Philip Godfrey
(b. 1964)

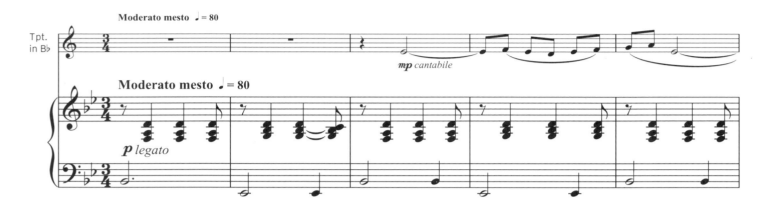